FROM DUST
to Hope

written by Mary Kaiser Donev
illustrated by Kathryn Prewett

**McGraw-Hill
School Division**

New York   Farmington

Frances would never forget the day she saw the dust storm coming. It blew across the Oklahoma plain like a gigantic black blizzard. She ran toward the house to warn her family. "Dad! Mom! Another dust storm!" she hollered.

Her father looked out from where he sat atop the tractor, the long furrows of the plowed field stretching out behind him. He was distressed. It was happening again.

Her mother was hanging sheets on the clothesline in the yard when she saw the 7,000-foot-high cloud roll toward them like a plague of locusts. Frances saw a look of despair in her mother's eyes.

Frances helped her mother yank the sheets from the line and then they ran for cover in the house as they had countless times before. Her father jumped from the tractor and followed close behind. They all knew if they didn't beat the storm the day would turn black as night. They wouldn't be able to see a thing and might not be able to find their way to the house.

It seemed as though the house was now a huge sieve as the dust whirled brutally against the sides of the building. Dust sifted under doorways and around windows, despite the rags Frances's mother tried to stuff along the cracks. They couldn't stop it! The dishes and shelves in their cupboards were covered in a thick layer of dust. It floated through the air into her closet and all over her clothes. Dust covered her bed sheets and blankets and her only doll.

It was 1935, and Frances could hardly recall a time in her ten years of life when the dust hadn't been there.

That night as they sat around the dinner table, the dust in the air made every morsel taste gritty, but she had learned to tolerate the feel of the dirt on her tongue and barely noticed it was there.

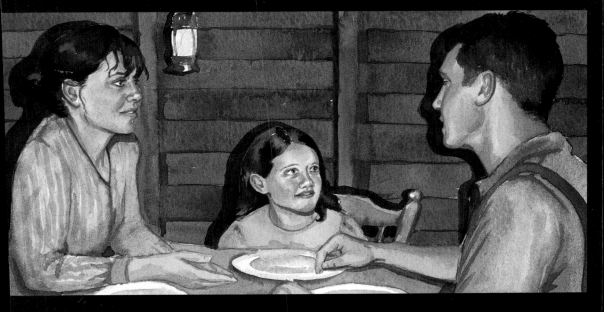

"We've got to move," Frances's father told her. "Your mother and I have discussed it. We're going to California."

Frances was speechless! She couldn't believe her father was willing to leave their farm as so many of their friends and neighbors had.

"The stifling heat and lack of water during this long drought have scorched and shriveled our crops," her father continued. "We can't go on like this. I got a letter yesterday from your Uncle Ned and he says we can join him out there and we'll find work in the fields. We're packing up and moving tomorrow."

"But, Dad," Frances said, sounding insistent, "we can't just leave everything and move to California. This is our home! I don't want to move!"

Frances's mother leaned across the table, stroking her daughter's brown hair.

"Frances, I know this is difficult for you. It's difficult for all of us, but it will be all right," her mother reassured her. "We're used to hardship, but this succession of storms is getting to be too much. We have to move where I won't always be worrying about you getting dust pneumonia or asthma or some other sickness from breathing air that isn't clean. I'm exhausted from having to clean up dust from morning until night. Your father can't cultivate the crops anymore. We're leaving tomorrow."

That had all been weeks before. They had packed what they could of their belongings on their farm truck. What they couldn't tie down in the bed of the old, black pickup, they had sold or given away. It was a clumsy load, laden with chairs and mattresses piled high on top of it.

It was a long and tedious journey across the country toting all their possessions. The truck was old and the engine ran poorly from the dust that had worked its way inside over the years. It had broken down many times along the way, seemingly incapable of driving another mile. Frances's father had always managed to repair it and they would once again continue on their journey.

At last they crossed into California.

"Your Uncle Ned and the rest of his family are working in the fields outside Bakersfield," Frances's father announced as he turned into a small service station just past the border. "We'll make our way there, but first, I have to stop to buy gas."

Pulling to a stop near the fuel pumps, he climbed out of the truck. A man emerged from inside the building, and asked, "Can I help you?"

"We just need some gas," Frances's father replied. "About five dollars should do it."

The man squinted at the inscription on the vehicle's license, and at the bulging truck bed overflowing with household goods, with an undisguised look of disgust on his face.

"We don't sell gas to your kind. Go back to Oklahoma where you came from. You're not welcome here in California."

Frances was shocked at the rude way the man had spoken to her father. She yearned to be back home where people were considerate and would never address anyone with such disrespect.

Her father did not hurl an insult at the man in return. He merely responded deliberately and calmly. "Much obliged, sir. I think we'll just drive down the road a bit and find us some gas there."

Opening the door of the truck, her father climbed back in and started the engine without saying another word.

They found a station a few miles further on that would sell them gas, but only when the owner insisted on getting the money in advance. This was not the reception Frances expected to receive when her parents had spoken of California, the land of opportunity.

A day later they located Uncle Ned, Aunt Helen and their twelve-year-old twin boys, Emil and Al. The family lived in a small house near the fields where they helped harvest grapes.

When Frances and her parents pulled up in front of the house after dark, the entire clan rushed out to meet them and hugs were exchanged all around. Frances was thrilled to see her favorite aunt.

Later, as Frances sat drinking a cup of warm milk, she recounted what had happened at the gas station to her aunt.

"How could he put up with that man talking to him that way?" Frances wanted to know.

"Many people don't like us coming here," Aunt Helen explained to Frances. "Their first inclination is not to like us because we talk with a different accent. They think we're going to take jobs away from them. They call us a lot of names, like Okie, to insult us. But don't you mind that. There's nothing wrong with who you are and where you come from.

"Lots of people are good to us here, and your father and mother will be able to work again without all that dust blowing everywhere. Now, you drink your milk and get ready for bed."

In the next few weeks, as she worked alongside her parents in the field picking grapes, Frances thought a great deal about what her aunt had said.

One day, her mother told her it was time for her to start school. Frances was nervous about attending a new school. She longed to make friends her own age, but how would the kids here react to her, an Okie?

On the first day of school, Frances and her twin cousins walked together up to the steps of the small schoolhouse.

"Hey, you! Okies!" a boy mocked them with a fake Oklahoma twang. "Why don't you all go back to the dust fields where you belong?"

Emil clenched his fists and turned, ready for battle. No one was going to talk to them that way! Al looked as though he was ready to join in and slug the boy. A small circle of students gathered around them. Frances had no idea how to restrain her cousins. There was undoubtedly going to be a fight!

Frances thought back to Aunt Helen's words. She turned and faced the boy, looking him straight in the eyes.

"There's nothing wrong with who I am or where I come from," she responded calmly. "I'm proud to be from Oklahoma. Just as I'm proud now to be from California."

Frances's heart pounded in her chest. She didn't know what the boy or her cousins would do next.

A girl in a pale blue dress stepped out from the crowd.

"I'd say we're pretty lucky to have these nice people from Oklahoma," she said addressing the crowd of students.

"They certainly seem to have a lot better manners than Harvey here does," she added, pointing to the boy who had insulted Frances and her cousins.

The children began to laugh. Harvey held up a threatening fist, turned bright red and ran away.

The girl walked up to Frances. "I'm Cassie," she said as she held out her hand. "Welcome to your new school."

Frances thought back to what Aunt Helen had said. "Lots of people are good to us here."

She extended her own hand to grasp Cassie's.

Frances looked into Cassie's dark blue eyes. She knew that she had made her first California friend and, as her mother had promised, things really were going to be all right.